One day, Lotty creeps past Kevin
and Wellington asleep in the
kennel. She goes out of the
farmyard and down the road.

1

She can smell a fox. She runs
along the road picking up the
smell. Then suddenly the smell
has gone.

Lotty goes up and down the road hunting for the smell. She picks it up by the gap in the hedge.

Lotty creeps into the field. The smell of the fox is strong. Lotty runs after the smell again.

Then she sees the cows in the field. She stops running. She sees that the cows are watching her.

The cows start to come to Lotty.

They start to run to her. Oh no!

They are big cows.

Lotty runs out of the field as fast
as she can. She is huffing and
puffing when she gets to the road.

The cows come to a stop just before the hedge. Lotty thanks her lucky stars that the cows are too big for the gap.